MANY MILES

The Arabs

Tana Reiff

A Pacemaker® **HOPES** *and* **DREAMS 2** Book

FEARON/JANUS/QUERCUS
Belmont, California

Simon & Schuster Supplementary Education Group

HOPES *and* DREAMS 2

Cover photo: Arab American Collection, National Museum
             of American History/Smithsonian Institution
Cover Design: Rucker Huggins
Illustration: Duane Bibby

ISBN 0-8224-3804-6
Library of Congress Catalog Card Number: 92-71065

Printed in the United States of America
1. 9 8 7 6 5 4 3
MA

CONTENTS

1 Dreams of Gold
Mt. Lebanon, Syria,* 1902

"You should have seen him!"
said Mama.
"Your uncle came back
from America
looking so rich!
He was wearing a suit!
Think of it!
He had a big gold watch.
And his shoes!
They tied up the front
and had a bright shine."

Her son, Habib Malouf,
had never seen
American clothes.
He most often had on
a large robe.

*The present-day country of Lebanon,
including the Mt. Lebanon area, was
a part of Syria in 1902.

His shoes were soft,
and his feet
slipped into them
with no strings to tie.
Sometimes he wrapped
a long piece of cloth
around and around his head.
To dress up,
he put on pants
that looked like two large bags
pulled together at each foot.
He believed that his uncle
must have looked
very, very different.

"Why did Uncle
go to America?"
young Habib asked his mother.

"He went for the Expo,"
explained Mama.
"It was a big show
of many fine things
from around the world.
Uncle showed the Americans
the pots and bowls we make."

"A group from our village
is going to America,"
Habib told Mama.
"They will stay
for two years.
They will work hard
and get rich, too.
Then they will come home.
I want to go along
to pick gold from the trees!"

"But you are only 16,"
said Mama.

"I will share my money
with our whole family!"
said Habib.

"I don't know,"
said Mama.
She shook her head.
"You are big for your age.
But you are still a boy."

"Please, Mama,"
said Habib.

"I'll be back
in two years."

"Well, if you go,
be careful,"
said Mama.
"America is
a very strange place."

Two weeks later,
45 people from the village
were ready to leave.
Mama put her arms
around her son.
Habib felt her press something
into his hand.
"Here is a little pocket money,"
Mama whispered.
"I know it will return
ten times over."

The group of Arabs
from the village
set out on foot
across the mountains.

Their ship was waiting
at the port of Beirut.

For three weeks,
Habib and the others
were on that ship.
They were crowded
under the main deck.
They could not wash.
Some people were sick.
The smell was worse
than any Habib had ever known.
He wished he could sleep
to pass the time.
He had no idea
what lay ahead
in America.
But he tried his best
to keep his mind
on dreams of gold.

Thinking It Over

1. If you believed
   that you could get rich
   by going to a far-away place,
   would you go?

2. What do you think
   will happen to Habib
   in America?

3. Have you ever tried
   to get your mind off something
   by thinking about something else?

2 Fadil's Settlement

There were Arabs
living in New York City
when Habib got there.
Many of the people
from Habib's village
stayed in New York.
But right away Habib knew
he did not want to live
in the big city.
He did not want
to work in a factory.
"I would feel
like a man in chains,"
he said to himself.

He heard stories
of other men and women
from his country.
They had headed west
to become peddlers.
They went on the road

to sell all kinds of things
from farm to farm
and town to town.

"This is the life for me,"
said young Habib.

He made his way west
with the money
his mother had given him.
He started out
on the train.
Part of the way
he walked.
Now and then he paid
for a wagon ride.
He saw many trees.
None of them
had gold on them.

At last he came upon
a settlement of other Arabs.
They were all peddlers.
One of them
was a young woman
with beautiful dark eyes.

She smiled when she saw
Habib looking at her.

A tall man named Fadil
came up to Habib.
"That's Selwa,"
said Fadil.
"She first came here
about a year ago.
I taught her
how to be a peddler.
She learned fast.
I can teach you
the ways of the road, too."

Fadil ran the settlement.
He gave the peddlers
a home off the road.
He sold them things
to take out and sell.
To Habib,
Fadil was a green spot
in the desert.

Fadil handed Habib
a large bag.

"This is your pack,"
Fadil explained.
"You carry your goods in it.
It will be very heavy.
But if you do well,
it will be very light
at the end of a trip."

Fadil hung it
over Habib's back.
He began to fill the pack
with all kinds of things.
Ribbon, lace, and needles.
Cloth, clothing, and cups.
Pots and pans and bowls.
Jewelry and little toys.
Habib would carry
just the kinds of things
the people needed
out in the country.

Then Fadil began
to tell Habib
how to do business.
"You go up and knock
on the door,"

he told the young man.
"First off, you say,
'How do you do?'.
Try to say that in English."

"How do you do?"
said Habib.

"Very good,"
said Fadil.

"Then you say,
'Beautiful day,
isn't it, ma'am?'.
You say that
even if it is raining!"
said Fadil.
"Then you say,
'My, what a pretty child
you have there, ma'am.'
And you give a little toy
to the child.
You take no money for it."

"Give the toy free?"
asked Habib.

"Yes, you do,"
said Fadil.
"Then you say,
'And wouldn't the lady
enjoy a nice, new pot
to cook in tonight?'"

Habib pulled out a pot
to show how he would do it.

"And then, young man,
you wait for a minute,"
said Fadil.
"Before you know it,
the lady of the house
will ask you what else
you have for sale.
You add everything up,
you take the money,
and you leave
with a lighter pack.
But before you go,
you always say,
'Have a very nice day!'"

"I see,"
said Habib.

"The last house of the day
is where you want to stay
for the night,"
Fadil went on.
He explained to Habib
how to ask for food
and a warm place to sleep.

With that,
Habib was on the road.
He remembered everything
that Fadil had told him.
And every night,
his heavy pack
was a few pounds lighter
than it was that morning.

Thinking It Over

1. Why is it a good sign
   that Habib's pack
   was lighter each night?

2. In what jobs
   might someone teach you
   how to do the work?

3. Would you enjoy
   being a peddler?
   Why or why not?

3 On the Road

At first,
Habib did not understand
anything the farm women
said to him.
He would shake his head
as if he did understand.
He kept a smile on his face.
The women never knew
how little English
Habib could speak.
They just enjoyed
seeing his happy face
to break up the day.

All the while, however,
Habib listened
to the people speak.
Little by little,
he learned English.
Before very long,
he really did understand

what they said.
He could speak English, too,
even if he did not sound
like an American.
In fact, the time came
when he did not need
to give out free toys.
Instead, he told stories
to the children.

Habib could hear
the children's cries of joy
all the way
from the end
of each farm lane.
"Look, Mother!"
a child would shout.
"Habib is coming!"

"How are you today?"
Habib would ask
when he got to the door.
"I have a new story for you!"

"Put down your pack,"
the mother would say.

Habib, the children,
and sometimes the mother
would all sit together
on the front porch.
Then Habib would begin
to tell one of his stories.

Really, they were old stories.
He had heard them
when he was a child.
He told stories
of magic lamps
and sailors at sea
and beautiful princesses.
The farm children
hung onto every word.
After the story,
the mother almost always
bought the things she needed.
Habib made not only money
but many friends, too.

One day,
as he turned into a lane,
he heard the sound
of a child's scream.

Mrs. Gates came running
out of the house.

"You are here
just in time!"
she cried.
"My little girl
fell down the well!
Can you help?"

Habib threw down his pack.
He ran toward the well.
The closer he got,
the louder the scream became.

"I can't get the bucket
down into the well,"
cried Mrs. Gates.
"I don't know
what is wrong."

Habib could see
that the rope tied to the bucket
was stuck.
It was very easy
to free the rope.

He let the bucket
down into the well.
"Grab the bucket,"
he called to the child.

The little girl
reached for the bucket.

"Climb in the bucket now,"
said Habib.
He felt the child's weight
at the bottom of the well.
Then Habib pulled the rope.
The little girl
came up in the bucket,
safe and sound.

"How can I thank you?"
Mrs. Gates asked.
Tears ran down her face.

"It was nothing!"
said Habib.

"You must stay here
every time you pass this way,"

said Mrs. Gates.
"Plan on it!"

On many other nights,
Habib ended up in a cold barn
or on wet grass.
Some days,
he had to walk for hours
under a hot, dry sun.
Other days he walked
in snow and ice.
Sometimes he got lost.
More than once he was robbed.
Much of the time
Habib was alone.
As he walked the roads,
a picture of Selwa,
the beautiful young peddler,
often came into his mind.

But one night each month,
Habib was not alone.
He stayed at the Gates home.
As months went by,
he made friends like this
all over the land.

Thinking It Over

1. Have you ever done something
   for someone
   that they will never forget?
   How did you feel?

2. Why might something
   be easy for one person
   that another person could not do?

3. What are some ways
   that a person might learn English
   besides going to school?

4 Two Brave Peddlers

When Habib needed a rest,
or more things to sell,
he made his way
back to the settlement.
It was always good
to get back with his people
for a few days.

Here, in the big kitchen,
the peddlers
could eat together
and play cards
late into the night.
They could drink and laugh.
They could speak in Arabic
and sing old Arabic songs.
They could be themselves.

Habib saw Selwa
in the kitchen
with the other peddlers.

"I have a story
to tell you all,"
said Habib.
They all enjoyed
each other's stories.
Habib's stories
were always the best.
He told the group
about helping the girl
get out of the well.

"You were very brave,"
said Selwa.

"It was nothing,"
said Habib.
"I think *you* are brave!
It is hard to believe
that a beautiful young woman
such as yourself
goes out on the road alone."

"I am no more afraid
than any man,"
said Selwa.
"I know there is money

to be made
as a peddler.
I want to make money
as much as you do.
I can stand the road
just fine, thank you."

"Perhaps you and I
could go on the road together
next time out,"
said Habib.

"How would we decide
who gets the money?"
Selwa asked.

"We could get married,"
said Habib.
"Then all that is mine
will be yours, too.
And all that is yours
will be mine, as well.
We will help each other,
on the road and off!"

Selwa smiled.
Her large, dark eyes
began to shine.
"All right,"
she said.
"Let's get married.
We will work together."

From that day on,
Habib and Selwa Malouf
were a team.
It was nice
to have company
on those long trips
along the country roads
of America.

Thinking It Over

1. Do you believe
   that for married people
   "all that is mine
   is yours, too"?

2. How safe would it be today
   for a woman alone
   to walk country roads
   all by herself?

3. Would you rather travel alone
   or with another person?

5 Married Life

Habib pointed his finger
at the "Y" in the road.
"You go this way
and I'll go that way,"
he said to Selwa.
"We'll meet again
in the next town
over the hill."

With that,
the two of them set out
with their heavy packs.
They each did their selling
on their own.
But at the end of each day,
it was nice
to have someone
to talk to.
Habib and Selwa
were not only married.
They were also best friends.

They tried to meet
every night.
But some nights
it was very cold.
On those nights,
it was best
to stay in different homes
than to be together
out in the cold.

But one very cold night
they were together.
"We must find
an inside place to sleep,"
said Selwa.

They were deep in the woods.
The night was black
but for the snow
that flew in their faces.
They could not see
where they were going.

"I think I see
a little house over there,"
said Habib.

They made their way
to the little stone house.
No light came from it.
"It looks as if
no one lives here,"
said Selwa.

They walked inside.
It was so dark
that Habib tripped
over something.
"There seem to be
two long beds in here,"
he said.

They put down their packs.
They each lay down on a bed
and went to sleep.

The next morning,
the sun shot its light
into the little stone house.
Selwa popped up,
wide awake.
She screamed.
"Habib, look where we are!"

Habib, too, woke up.
"This is not a house!"
he said.
"It's a place
for dead people!
We spent the night
sleeping on graves!"

They grabbed their packs
and ran as fast as they could.
They didn't stop
until they were out
of the woods.

"That does it!"
said Habib.
"I am ready
to lay down my pack.
We have enough money
to buy a horse and buggy.
Let's stop walking
and take the next step
in our business."

"Yes, let's!"
said Selwa.

"We can pack the buggy
with things to sell.
We can leave
just enough space
for us to sleep.
I can't wait!"

So that is what they did.
With the horse and buggy,
Habib and Selwa
could travel more miles
in a day.
They could sell more
because they covered more ground.
It was so much better
to have a place to sleep,
even if it was only a buggy.

Best of all,
Habib and Selwa
were making lots of money.
They hoped to be rich
by the time they returned
to their home country.

Thinking It Over

1. Have you ever been
   "on the road"?
   What's a good story
   from your trip?

2. When do you know
   it is time
   to move on
   to something new—
   to take the next step?

3. What do you think
   will happen to Habib and Selwa
   in the days ahead?

6 Big Ideas

All next year,
Habib and Selwa Malouf
were on the road.
They liked working together.
But a big change was coming.
Selwa was going to have
a baby.
She wanted to start a home.
So they found a little house
in a town in Indiana.

When the baby came,
Selwa had to stop working.
While she stayed home
with baby Alice,
Habib went out selling
in the horse and buggy.
Once again,
he was on the road
by himself.

He missed Selwa.
He missed being able
to see his baby girl
grow day by day.
But being on the road alone
gave Habib time to think.
He began to think
that he should save up
and buy a truck.
Trucks that ran without a horse
were something new.
Habib dreamed
of riding along these roads
in his new truck.
Oh, how many miles
he could cover in a day,
if only he had a truck!

And maybe after that
he could open a dry-goods store.
He and Selwa
could sell cloth and thread
and things for the home,
much as he did now.
He could get off the road.
He could see his family

any time he wanted to.
He could make more money
than he ever dreamed of.
He couldn't wait
to tell Selwa his ideas.
When he got home
the next time,
she met him at the door.

"I must tell you
all about my ideas!"
said Selwa.

"Your ideas?"
said Habib.
"I have ideas, too.
You tell yours first."

"I have been seeing
big trucks on the street,"
she began.
"They run with no horses!
Why, we could fill them
with things to sell!
I think we should buy one
as soon as we can!"

Habib began to laugh.
"We may have been
in two different places,"
he said.
"But we have had
the same idea!
Did you also have
the idea about the store?"

"Yes, I did!"
Selwa said.
"Every week
someone opens a new store
in this little town.
Maybe someday
we could open a dry-goods store!"

Habib laughed some more.
He gave his wife a big kiss.
"Ah, how I love you!"
he said.
"We are two people
of like minds!"

"There is one problem,"
Selwa said.

"We both told our parents
we would come home
after two years."

"How can we go home
when we are so busy
getting rich?"
said Habib.

That night,
he wrote his mother
a long letter.
The beautiful bends and turns
of his Arabic writing
filled five pages.
"I will always love you,"
the letter ended.
"But my wife and I
must stay in America.
Our life here
is too good to leave!"
Then he folded some money
along with the letter.
It was ten times more
than Mama had given him
the day he left Mt. Lebanon.

Thinking It Over

1. Do you have
   any big plans
   for the years ahead?

2. Do you believe
   that Habib and Selwa's plans
   will work out?

3. What does it mean
   to be "of like minds"
   with another person?

7 Becoming American

Selwa couldn't believe her eyes
the day Habib drove up
in a truck.
It was not new.
The person who owned it
wanted a new truck.
So Habib got a good price
on the old one.
Even so,
it had taken years
to save up enough money.

The funny thing was,
once Habib had the truck,
he didn't drive very far.
He did most of his business
in and around town.
He would drive
up and down the streets.
He would stop on each block.
People would step right up

into the truck
and take a look
at what was for sale.

Or, Habib would drive
out to the farms
and back again
in the same day.
Most nights,
he was home
with his family—
Selwa, Alice, and young Philip.

With Habib around more,
he and Selwa
became more interested
in being part of the town.
They were Christians,
so they joined a church.
They became interested
in town business matters.
They began doing
the same things
their American neighbors did.
And they spoke English,
even at home.

One Saturday morning,
Selwa heard some music
coming from outside.
She looked out the window.
"Look, everyone!"
she called to the family.

Habib and the children
came over to find out
what the noise was.
They saw the town band
marching down the street.
The band was playing
happy American songs.
It was a parade.

"It's the Fourth of July!"
said Habib.

"I know that,"
said Alice.
"Yesterday was the third.
So today is the fourth."

"The Fourth of July
is a big day for Americans,"

Habib explained
to the child.
"That was the day
America told the world
it was going to be
a free country."

"So that is what
the parade is all about,"
said Alice.
"It looks like fun!"

The whole family
ran outside.
The children
joined in the parade.
They marched
behind the town band.
Someone handed each child
an American flag.

"Look at that!"
said Selwa.
"Our children are waving
American flags!"

"They are Americans,"
said Habib.

"Why do you look so sad?"
Selwa asked her husband.

"Sometimes I think
we should become Americans,"
he said.
"We live here.
We make money here.
We are as free as birds
in this country."

"But remember,"
Selwa said,
"we did not come here
to become Americans.
We came here to get rich
and then go home."

"But with every new day,
our roots in America
grow deeper,"
said Habib.

"It is the way
our life is turning out."

"I suppose you are right,"
said Selwa.
"I will think about it.
I will think
about becoming an American."

When the Fourth of July
came around the next year,
Habib and Selwa
marched in the town parade.
They and their children
all waved American flags.
By that next year
Habib and Selwa Malouf
had become full American citizens.

Thinking It Over

1. What does being
   an American citizen
   mean to you?

2. How is America
   different from the country
   that you or someone you know
   came from?
   How is it better?
   How is it not better?

3. What do you think
   is the best part
   about being an American citizen?

8 The Little Book

By the time
Habib and Selwa
opened their store,
their children were old enough
to help out.
Alice helped out
in the store.
Philip drove the truck
to take goods
right to people's homes.
Because the whole family
worked in the business,
the store could stay open
more hours in a day.
And because they lived
next door to the store,
someone could be there
almost always.

Around the same time,
a new book came out.

Habib and Selwa
were interested in the book
because it was written
by an Arab-American
named Kahlil Gibran.
The little book
was called *The Prophet*.
It was full of things
to think about.

Sometimes when Habib
had been working all day,
he would feel tired.
He would pull out the book.
"Work is love,"
wrote Gibran.
"All work is empty
save when there is love . . .
Weave the cloth with threads
drawn from your heart . . ."

These words helped Habib
to feel strong again.
He put love
into his work.
And it paid off.

The dry-goods store
did very, very well.

By 1929,
Habib and Selwa began to talk
about buying a bigger house.
But it was not to happen.
Some very bad news
got in the way.
The stock market crash
in October 1929
changed everything.

Half the people
in the town
were out of work.
It was hard for them
to pay their bills.
This was not the time
to buy new things.
It was not the time
to make new clothes
out of things
the Maloufs sold.
People had to make do
with what they already had.

"Our business
is in big trouble,"
Habib told Selwa one day.
"I don't know how
we can stay open
much longer."

"But everything
was going so well!"
cried Selwa.

"Everything is different,"
said Habib.
"We can't look at life
the way we could before.
We felt so happy before.
Now we feel sad.
Gibran says
we only know
what it is to be happy
from knowing what it is
to be sad."

"But our dreams
have gone up in smoke,"
said Selwa.

"I am sure
that we will be happy
on another day,"
Habib said.
"There is nothing we can do
but find a way
to keep on going
until that day comes."

It was very hard
for Habib and Selwa
to do what they did next.
They decided
they had to close the store.
They both cried
when they locked
the store's front door
that cold winter day.

And so,
during most of the 1930s,
Habib and Selwa
did what they had to do.
They went out on the road.
Once again,
they were peddlers.

Thinking It Over

1. Did you ever read a book
   that made you
   think about things?
   What was the book called?

2. What have you
   had to decide to do
   that was really hard?

3. Have you ever had a dream
   "go up in smoke"?
   How did things work out?

9 Better Times

This time out,
Habib and Selwa
had their truck.
Still, life on the road
was not easy.
And now,
Habib and Selwa
were older.

Alice and Philip,
who were not children now,
stayed back in Indiana.
They both got married
and started their own families.

Habib and Selwa
did not get rich
on the road.
They did make enough money
to keep the house
in Indiana.

They were also able
to put some money away.
"We will open
another store,"
Habib kept on saying.

By the end of the 1930s,
the country's money problems
were better.
People were working again.
Habib and Selwa
were once again ready
to open a dry-goods store.

By that time,
the little town in Indiana
was more like
a small city.
"I think we should open
a bigger store this time,"
said Habib.
"The time is right."

They found a place
on the town square.
It was not too large.

But there was space
on the upper floors
for the business to grow.

And it did grow.
Over the next 20 years,
the dry-goods store
became a department store.
What had started
with cloth and thread
and things for the home
was now much more.
On the first floor
there were jewelry, shoes,
candy, and books.
Clothing for the whole family
was on the upper floors.
Downstairs there was
anything one could think of
for the home.

And what had started
as one little old truck
was now a fleet of six.

Habib and Selwa
bought a big house
in a nice part
of the city.
Alice and Philip,
who worked for the store,
lived in big houses
with their families, too.
Every one of them
drove a big, new car.
And every week,
Habib sent a big check
to his mother.

"Look deep into your heart,"
Habib read from *The Prophet*.
"And you shall find
it is only that
which has given you sorrow
that is giving you joy."

"We had to be poor again
to know how good it is now,"
said Selwa.

Just then,
the phone rang.
It was Habib's younger brother
back in Mt. Lebanon.
Habib could not remember
the last time
he had heard his brother's voice.
It had been many years.

"Mama died last night,"
Habib's brother said.
"Don't come home.
You never came home
in almost 50 years.
Don't take the trouble now."

The brother's words
were sharp and angry.
Habib felt bad.
"You are right,"
he told his brother.
"There is nothing
I can do now.
I am sorry."

Thinking It Over

1. Can a person ever be
   completely happy?
   Why or why not?

2. What is your idea
   of "making it" in life?

3. If you were Habib,
   what would you have done
   when your mother died?

10 An Arab-American Star

A few years later,
Habib got another important call.
It was from Mike Tamer.
He was a business friend
who headed a group
of Arab-American clubs.

"Have you heard
of the funny man
named Danny Thomas?"
Mike asked Habib.

"Oh, sure,"
said Habib.
"He's on TV,
and he used to be on radio.
He's Lebanese, you know."

"Oh, yes, I know.
He's an old friend of mine,"
said Mike.

"Well, Danny has a dream.
He wants to start
a children's hospital
named after St. Jude.*
He's asking people
to give money
to get it off the ground.
But it's going to take
a lot of money
to keep the hospital running.
Now, this hospital
is not just for Arab-Americans.
But we want to start
an Arab-American group
to make sure the hospital
can always keep running."

Habib was interested.
"America has been good to me,"
he said to Mike.
"This might be a way
to give something back
to this great country."

*The full current name is St. Jude
 Children's Research Hospital.

"That's what I think, too,"
said Mike.
"You are a top business man.
We need you."
He asked Habib
to come to a meeting.

"I will be happy
to join this cause,"
said Habib.

The day came.
Habib went to Chicago.
One hundred Arab-Americans
went to the meeting.
Among them
were Arab Christians
as well as Muslims.
A doctor stood up and said
the hospital would be
for very sick children.
It didn't matter
if the children were poor.
St. Jude would be there
to help them.

Then Danny Thomas
stood up to speak.
He told the story
of his dream for a hospital.
Before he became famous,
he had asked St. Jude
to help him decide
if he should keep trying
to make it in show business.
"Help me find
my place in life,"
he had begged.
"If you do,
I will build something
that will give hope
to people who need it."

Danny Thomas
got his own show
in the early days of television.
He became a big star.
Now it was time for him
to give something back.
Danny told
of his plans for the hospital.

The people at the meeting
started a new group called ALSAC.
The letters stood for
*American Lebanese Syrian
Associated Charities.*

"I will go out
and start groups
all over the country,"
Habib told Mike Tamer.
"They will all be part of ALSAC."

Yet again,
Habib was on the road.
This time, however,
the money he drummed up
was not for himself
or his family.
It was for the hospital
and Danny Thomas's dream.

Habib remembered
another part of *The Prophet—*
"It is when
you give of yourself
that you truly give."

Habib felt good
about the time he gave
for St. Jude.

It was fun, too.
Sometimes Danny himself
would show up
at meetings here and there.
After the meetings,
everyone would play cards.
By early morning
everyone was broke.
Everyone, that is,
except St. Jude.

And the dances!
Habib put together "Hafli Nights."
Arab-Americans came
from all around.
As American as they lived,
their Middle Eastern dance
called *hafli*
was a little piece of home.

Thinking It Over

1. Have you ever banded together
   with other people
   to work for a cause?

2. What ways do you know of
   to raise money?

3. If someone asked you
   to help out with a cause,
   what would make you
   say "yes"?

11 A Night to Remember

Habib blew
into the house
like a shot of winter wind.
"Selwa, we are going
to Memphis, Tennessee!"
he said.

"What's going on?"
Selwa wanted to know.

"Danny Thomas
is putting on
a big, big show!"
said Habib.
"We can't miss it!
Big Hollywood stars
will be there!
Pack your bags!"

They flew down
to Memphis,

where the hospital
would be built.
They checked into a hotel.
Then they headed
for the big show.

"You didn't tell me
it would be outside,"
said Selwa
when they got there.
"The sky is black.
What if it rains?"

"I can just hear
Danny's voice,"
laughed Habib.
"He would say,
'St. Jude might hear you.
It isn't going to rain.'"

The ugly black clouds
rolled across the sky.
The sky grew darker
by the minute.
But it didn't rain.
Then, all of a sudden,

the black sky parted.
Between two giant clouds
hung a C-shaped moon
and one bright star.

The show went on.
Not a drop of rain
fell on the crowd.

At the end,
Danny Thomas came out
to say a word.
"If any of you people here
don't think that this project
has been touched
by the hand of God,
I beg you
to look up
into the sky."

There were the black clouds
with the moon and star
between them.
Nothing had moved
during the whole show.
Habib began to clap,

then Selwa.
Then the huge crowd
broke out clapping
along with them.
What a night!

The minute they left,
the rain came down
in sheets.

Habib and Selwa
got caught in the storm.
They had gone
to say hello to Danny.
As Selwa spoke with him,
Habib wrote a big check
and handed it over.

"God bless you!"
Danny said.
"And I want to see you here
when the hospital opens!"

"We'll be here!"
said Habib.

Thinking It Over

1. Why do you think
   the rain held off
   until after the show?

2. Has anything like this
   ever happened to you?

3. Do you think
   that if you believe enough
   in something,
   it will happen?

12 The Hospital Opens

Nothing could keep Habib
away from Memphis
when the hospital
was ready to open.
It was 1962.
Habib and Selwa
were getting old.
But Danny Thomas's dream
had become Habib's dream too.

Habib was ready to leave
two days early.
He walked up and down
the rows in the store.
"I'm going to Memphis!"
he told every worker.
"I wouldn't miss it
for the world!"
Some of them
looked at him
as a silly old man.

The next day,
he woke up
with a bad cold.
"You're staying in bed,"
said Selwa.

"Half a day
and I'll be fine!"
said Habib.

He felt no better
by the end of the day.
It was the night before
the trip to Memphis.
"You can't go,"
said Selwa.

"Nothing will stop me!"
Habib told her.

Selwa knew
it was no use
trying to stop him.
He would go even
if it killed him.
The next morning,

the two of them
were on a plane
headed for Memphis.

The crowd
was already large
when Habib and Selwa
got to the new hospital.
They made their way
to the front.

Selwa was the first
to spot Danny Thomas.
"There he is!"
she cried.

Danny thanked everyone
for their work
for the new hospital.
"And now," he said,
"I have something
to show you all."
He pulled a black cloth
that covered something
behind him.
It was a statue

of St. Jude.
The statue stood
tall and proud.

And so did Habib.
"This great hospital
stands for us,"
he said.
"Do you remember
when some of us
used to think
that you could pick
gold from the trees
in America?"

"Oh, yes,"
Selwa laughed.

"We came many miles
from the Middle East,"
Habib went on.
"We walked many miles
along the country roads
of the farm states.
We drove many miles
to make our way

in this great country.
We covered many miles
to get the money
to build this hospital.
And we came many miles
to see this great day."

"We are proud,"
said Selwa.
"We have come
many, many miles
from where we started."

It was 25 years later
that Philip and his family
visited Memphis.
They came to see
a new building
beside the hospital.
Inside it were pictures
that told the story
of the Arab-Americans,
like Habib,
who helped to keep
the hospital going.